SEASHORE LIFE *of* EASTERN CANADA

A guide to identifying intertidal marine species

D1453770

JIM CORNALL *and* GENNY SIMARD

NIMBUS
PUBLISHING LTD

Nimbus Publishing Limited
3731 Mackintosh St, Halifax, NS B3K 5A5
(902) 455-4286 nimbus.ca

Printed and bound in Canada

NB1117

Cover and interior design: Jenn Embree

Library and Archives Canada Cataloguing in Publication

Cornall, Jim, 1963-, author
Seashore life of Eastern Canada : a guide to identifying intertidal marine species / Jim Cornall and Genny Simard.
Issued in print and electronic formats.
ISBN 978-1-77108-182-5 (pbk.).—ISBN 978-1-77108-183-2 (pdf)
1. Seashore animals—Canada, Eastern—Identification. 2. Seashore plants—Canada, Eastern—Identification. 3. Seashore biology— Canada, Eastern. I. Simard, Geneviève, 1966-, author II. Title.

QH106.C67 2014   578.769'909713   C2013-908098-8
                                                C2013-908099-6

Nimbus Publishing acknowledges the financial support for its publishing activities from the Government of Canada through the Canada Book Fund (CBF) and the Canada Council for the Arts, and from the Province of Nova Scotia through Film & Creative Industries Nova Scotia. We are pleased to work in partnership with Film & Creative Industries Nova Scotia to develop and promote our creative industries for the benefit of all Nova Scotians.

MIX
Paper from responsible sources
FSC® C103113

Contents

Introduction

If you have walked along a beach, whether on the coast of the Maritimes or a tropical island, you would have noticed a variety of plant and animal species, even if it was only a band of empty and broken shells along the tide line. But look more closely, and it is possible to find many fascinating creatures thriving in a zone greatly influenced by the tides.

The fact that the sea rises and falls continuously makes that part of the beach—the intertidal zone—a very harsh environment to live in. At the top of the intertidal zone, most of the species live with only the occasional splash from the rising tide. At the bottom end of the zone, species are only occasionally exposed. However, between these two extremes, animals and plants are subjected to periods when they are covered in water, and others when they are exposed. They are also subjected to rain, the heat of the sun, or extreme cold during winter. And, for some species, there is the danger of predation from mammals or birds. In order to live, many have adapted to life in this kind of environment.

So how do they survive?

Many species have evolved to have a shell on their backs, protecting them against both predation and desiccation. This also helps to maintain their shape when out of the water. Blue mussels and sea urchins, for

High tide (left), and low tide, in St. Andrews, NB, a difference of about 8 metres.

example, can continue to live at low tide with their internal organs very well protected inside a shell. Some animals take shelter under seaweed, rocks, or sand, where temperatures and humidity are more stable, thus avoiding desiccation and drastic changes in temperature until the water rises again. Tidal pools, which are created when seawater is left behind in a rocky basin at low tide, are also excellent shelters for organisms.

This guide focuses on the plants and animals most commonly found in the area covered with water at high tide and exposed at low tide. Every place on this planet affected by tides has this intertidal zone, although some, such as in the Bay of Fundy, have much greater tidal ranges than others.

With the information in this book, you will learn where to find these plants and animals at low tide: all you have to do is gently lift a rock, push aside a clump of seaweed, or dig in the sand to discover another world. But remember to always replace the rocks or seaweed in their original position, as they provide shelter to organisms we cannot always see.

Many mollusks live mostly in deeper waters—the subtidal zone—but their empty shells often wash up on shore. This is why we have included some subtidal species, living below the low tide level, as they are sometimes seen on beaches and tidal pools.

If you enjoy diving, you will have plenty of opportunities to observe some of these animals in their natural habitat. Wherever your travels take you, there will always be amazing plants and animals to discover.

There is a certain pleasure that comes from the ability to name the species we find, and with this book as your guide, you will be able to positively identify most of the creatures you discover on your shoreline adventures.

We have designed this guide so it is easy to use. The plants and animals that belong to the same family are grouped together. Some symbols replace lengthy text. A series of arrows on the images point to key characteristics for identifying a species. Each arrow has a number that corresponds to a more detailed description in the text found on the same page.

When necessary, close-up images of certain parts of the organism are shown to help in their identification. The majority of the species can be identified without the help of a hand-lens or microscope. However, a hand-lens is always a useful tool to carry while beachcombing.

Some interesting facts about each organism are also included in the text. At the top of each page, a map of the shore zones and a geographic map of the region show where each species can be found. This book covers the entire eastern Canadian coast, from Labrador to Nova Scotia and New Brunswick, going west into the Gulf and estuary of the St. Lawrence River.

THE PLANT AND ANIMAL PHYLA REPRESENTED IN THIS BOOK

PLANTS:

Chlorophyta: Green marine seaweed, mainly growing in the intertidal and shallow subtidal zones, as they require plenty of sunlight.

Phaeophyta: Brown marine seaweed that is sometimes tinged with olive green or yellow. They dominate the intertidal and shallow subtidal zones.

Rhodophyta: The 'red' seaweeds are generally purple or reddish brown, as opposed to bright red. To make it confusing, they can also sometimes have green or yellowish hues. In general, however, they are smaller than the browns, and found further down the beach, as their pigments allow photosynthesis while under water.

ANIMALS:

Porifera: Sponges consist of colonies of very simply organized cells that form a body which has neither a nervous system nor a digestive system. They filter seawater through layers of cells to trap nutritional elements.

Cnidaria: The cnidarians are simple animals that include jellies (which float around the water column) and anemones (fixed to a substrate). They show radial symmetry, for the most part, and very simple internal organs. They all have stinging cells with varying degrees of venom to catch their prey.

Ctenophora: On first looks, these animals are very similar to jellies, except they show 8 rows of comblike ciliary plates around their soft bodies. They do not have stinging cells, even though some of them have 2 tentacles. The shape of the body shows both radial and bilateral symmetry. Comb jellies, as they are called, are formidable predators, even cannibals.

Mollusca: Mollusks are soft-bodied animals with bilateral symmetry, with a large foot for moving around. Most have a calcareous shell for protection against predators and different climatic conditions. They include the sea slugs and snails (gastropods), and bivalves.

Arthropoda: The arthropods, including crustaceans like crabs, shrimps, and lobsters, are animals that have an external skeleton (shell) and jointed legs, and have a body divided into parts (head, thorax, and abdomen). This phylum of animals contains the largest number of species and individuals on the planet.

Echinodermata: The echinoderms, like seastars and sea urchins, are marine animals with a type of spiny skin. They have a somewhat radial symmetry and a water-vascular system to control the podia.

Some of the species have a shell made of calcareous plates. In order to feed, some filter water to capture plankton, while others are ferocious predators.

Chordata: Chordates are animals that have either a backbone (like fish), or a notochord (a supporting rod that some deem to be a primitive backbone). In this book, we mainly consider species that are part of the subphylum *urochordata* (the tunicates, like the sea peach). The larva of tunicates, before they become adults, all have a notochord. Once adults, they lose the notochord, and instead have a "tunic"—a kind of balloon-shaped skin—to support their internal organs. They all feed on plankton by filtering seawater using siphons.

WARNING

Even though some of the plants and animals listed in this book are considered edible, one has to be extremely careful before harvesting.

A "red tide" situation may occur, especially during hot summer months, which renders mollusks toxic to humans when consumed. A red tide is caused by an increase in certain microscopic algae producing marine biological toxins. Mollusks filter water to capture these algae as food. The toxins accumulate in the mollusks' bodies, but do not affect them. However, these toxins can cause severe illness, and even death, in humans. This is why some areas are closed to harvesting during certain times of the year.

Warning signs are generally placed in plain sight near beaches, but one can also contact the local office of the Department of Fisheries and Oceans to learn about the actual and current risks: dfo-mpo.gc.ca.

List of Symbols

In this book you will find two diagrams at the top of each page; one indicates which part of the shore you will most likely find the organism, and the other represents its geographical distribution.

THE SHORE IS DIVIDED INTO FIVE APPROXIMATE ZONES:

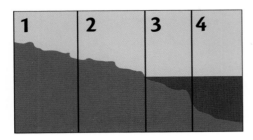 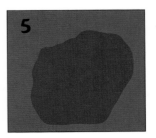

The upper intertidal zone (1):
From the high- to mid-tide level. At top of this zone, land is not affected by seawater, except for occasional spray.

The lower intertidal zone (2):
From the mid- to low-tide level.

Shallow subtidal zone (3):
The zone just below the low tide level, always in shallow waters.

Deep subtidal zone (4):
Deeper waters that often occur further offshore.

Tidal pools (5):
Formed by rocky basins that retain seawater when the tide goes out. Some animals that prefer deeper water sometimes shelter in tidal pools.

An orange band marks the zone(s) inhabited by the organism.

THE GEOGRAPHICAL DISTRIBUTION OF THE SPECIES IS MARKED IN BLUE ON THE MAPS, AND INCLUDES THE FOLLOWING:

1. Upper estuary (upriver)
2. Upper estuary (downriver)
3. Saguenay Fjord
4. Lower estuary (upriver)
5. Lower estuary (downriver)
6. Gulf of St. Lawrence (northern)
7. Gulf of St. Lawrence (southern)
8. Atlantic coast
9. Bay of Fundy

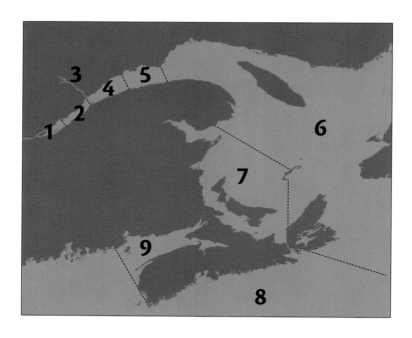

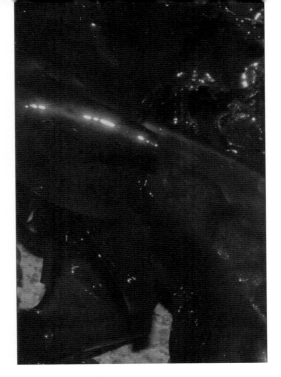

Chlorophyta

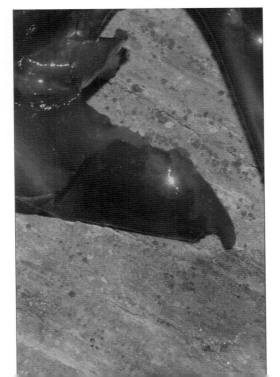

Sea lettuce
Ulva lactuca

This green seaweed has very thin, almost translucent fronds, and resembles green lettuce leaves. Sea lettuce has a short stalk between the fronds and the basal disk. The disk is used to attach the plant to rocks. Its colour varies from pale to dark green. It can reach a length of 1 metre.

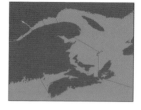

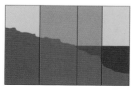

DISTRIBUTION:
Labrador to tropical regions, and from the upper estuary (upriver) to the Gulf of St. Lawrence.

HABITAT:
Lower intertidal and shallow subtidal zones.

Sea lettuce is an edible seaweed. It can often be seen floating on the surface of the water.

Phaeophyta

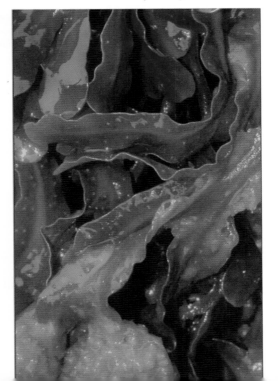

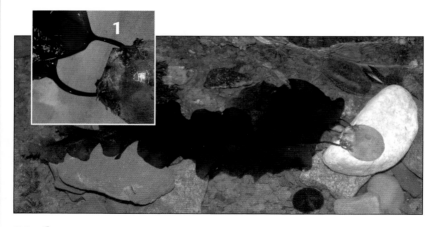

Kelp
Laminaria sp., Alaria sp.

Kelp is a brown seaweed with long blades that look like very long, flat ribbons. The stalk is rather stiff, with a holdfast shaped like a claw (1) for holding on to rocks. The blades can be either smooth or undulated, or even curled, and divided. They are brown or olive green. The blades can reach 2 metres or more in length.

DISTRIBUTION:
From the Arctic to Long Island Sound, and from the upper estuary (upriver) to the Gulf of St. Lawrence.

HABITAT:
Lower intertidal and subtidal zones.

Kelp form large forests under the oceans and greatly resist wave action. However, sea urchins often graze on them. After storms, kelp blades often wash up on shore. Several species are harvested in Canada for the food industry.

Knotted wrack
Ascophyllum nodosum

This brown seaweed has long narrow fronds, branching off in a "V" shape at regular intervals. Little air sacs (1) called air bladders can be seen on the fronds, which are used to help the seaweed float when the tide rises. A holdfast shaped like a claw at the base of the plant secures it to the rocks. The balloon-shaped reproductive receptacles (2) are yellow or brown. The colour of the branches varies from olive green to yellow green. It can reach 1.5 metres in length.

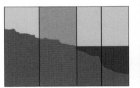

DISTRIBUTION:
From the Arctic to New Jersey and from the upper estuary (upriver) to the Gulf of St. Lawrence.

HABITAT:
Lower intertidal zone.

Knotted wrack is harvested in the Maritimes for the food industry, and has the largest biomass of any east coast seaweed.

Rockweed, Bladder wrack
Fucus vesiculosus

Rockweed, which falls into the brown seaweed group, has fronds branching off in a "V" shape, with a very obvious midrib. A series of pairs of air bladders are found along them. The reproductive receptacles (1) are balloon shaped, often with pointed extremities. The fronds are olive green, sometimes yellowish or dark green. Individual fronds can reach 90 cm.

DISTRIBUTION:
From the Arctic to North Carolina, and from the upper estuary (upriver) to the Gulf of St. Lawrence.

HABITAT:
Intertidal and the subtidal zones.

The multiple air bladders of the rockweed help to keep it vertical in the water column, allowing it to obtain as much sunlight as possible. The base of the plant keeps a hold of rocks, wharf pilings, saltwater marsh plants, and any other substrate.

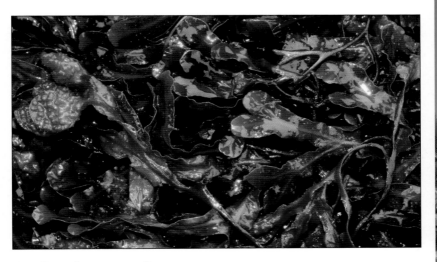

Spiral wrack
Fucus spiralis

The fronds of this brown seaweed are often spiralled and greatly resemble those of other rockweed. The balloon shape of the reproductive receptacles is round or forked, with a small margin all the way around. There are no air bladders. This seaweed is olive green, and can grow up to 30 cm.

DISTRIBUTION:
Newfoundland and Labrador to Long Island Sound, from the upper estuary (upriver) to the Gulf of St. Lawrence.

HABITAT:
Upper intertidal zone and in tidal pools.

On the shore, spiral wrack is generally found above the growing area of knotted wrack and rockweed, attached to rocks and wharf pilings, and sometimes floating in tide pools. It is exposed to the sun and sometimes harsh weather at low tide, but its surface against the sand is protected and kept moist and cool, which also serves as a shelter for many small intertidal creatures.

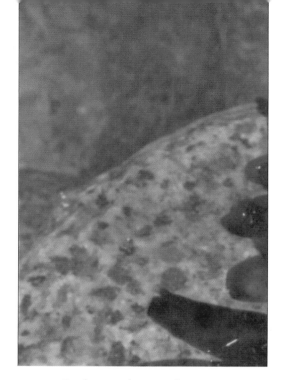

Rhodophyta

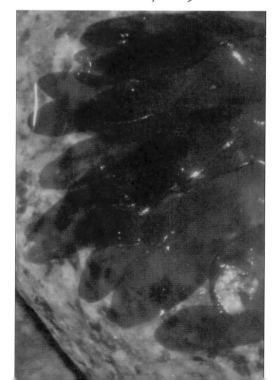

Irish moss, Carragheen
Chondrus crispus

With its frilled, flattened fronds forming many branches, this red seaweed attaches itself to rocks using a basal disk. Its colour varies a great deal: red, dark purple, brown, or green. It can reach 17 to 25 cm in length, depending on where it grows.

DISTRIBUTION:
From Labrador to Long Island Sound, and in the Gulf of St. Lawrence.

HABITAT:
Lower intertidal zone.

Irish moss is important commercially. It is harvested from beaches in great quantities and dried outdoors for food and medicinal purposes. This seaweed is rich in carrageenan, a substance used to stabilize products such as ice cream.

Dulse
Palmaria palmata,
Rhodymenia palmata

Dulse, a red seaweed with large blades lacking a midrib, has a holdfast that attaches the plant to rocks and other seaweed. The dark purple-red blades are thick and opaque, almost like rubber. This seaweed can measure up to 30 cm long.

DISTRIBUTION:
From the Arctic to Long Island Sound, and from the upper estuary to the Gulf of St. Lawrence.

HABITAT:
Lower intertidal and subtidal zones.

Dulse is harvested by hand in the Maritimes, especially on Grand Manan Island in the Bay of Fundy. It is sun-dried and eaten like chips, or used as a seasoning for seafood. It contains several nutritional elements.

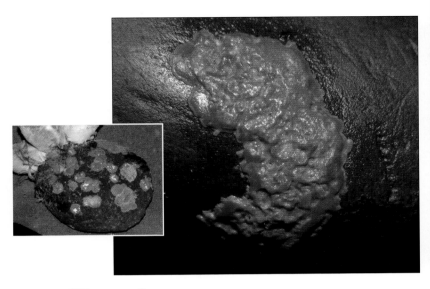

Coralline alga, encrusting pink alga
Lithothamnium sp.

This calcareous red algae covers large surfaces of rocks and shells like a thick, hard mineral crust. Its surface feels rough to the touch. It is generally is pink, with tinges of red.

DISTRIBUTION:
The St. Lawrence River and the whole eastern coast of North America.

HABITAT:
The subtidal zone to depths of 50 metres.

Coralline algae uses calcium carbonate to harden its cells. It grows very slowly, and it is resistant to grazing from urchins and limpets.

Porifera

Finger sponge
Haliclona oculata

This sponge species has slightly flattened or rounded finger-shaped branches. It is a yellow or greyish-brown colour, sometimes tinted with purple. It can reach 45 cm in length, with branches up to 12.5 cm thick.

DISTRIBUTION:
Labrador to Long Island Sound, and from the lower estuary to the Gulf of St. Lawrence.

HABITAT:
Occasionally in the lower intertidal, but mostly in the subtidal zone.

We often find specimens of finger sponge washed ashore. Once dried in the sun, it takes on the well-known texture of the sponges we use in the bath. It feeds by filtering water and plankton through multiple pores that completely cover its surface.

Crumb-of-bread sponge
Halichondria panicea

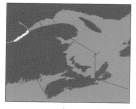

Sometimes covering a large surface area, this sponge species forms a crust on rocks below the water and resembles a spongy carpet. Its colour varies from brown, orange or yellow, to green. This sponge can cover an area of more than 1 square metre.

DISTRIBUTION:
The Arctic to Cape Cod, and from the lower estuary to the Gulf of St. Lawrence.

HABITAT:
Lower intertidal and subtidal zones.

The green colour on some of these sponges is caused by microscopic green algae living inside the colonies that form the crust.

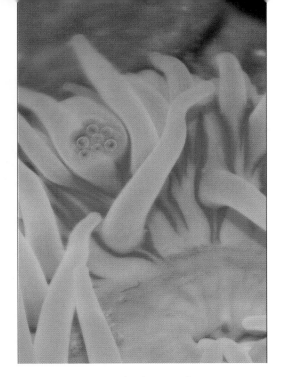

Cnidaria

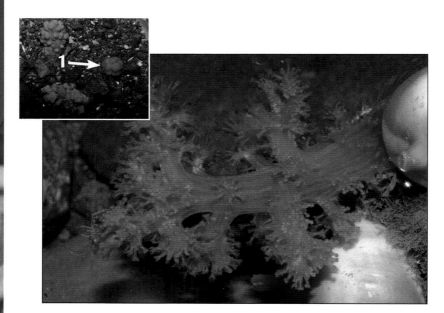

Red soft coral, Sea raspberry

Gersemia rubiformis

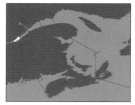

Red soft coral is a colony of polyps forming delicate branches from a main stem. When retracted, or out of the water, the organism resembles a raspberry (1). It ranges from pink to peach in colour. Growing to 12 cm in height, the colonies can reach 10 to 15 cm in diameter.

DISTRIBUTION:
From the Arctic to the Bay of Fundy, and from the upper estuary (downriver) to the Gulf of St. Lawrence.

HABITAT:
Subtidal zone.

Even though this species is called a coral, the red soft coral does not have the necessary system to produce calcium in order to form a reef. It always remains soft.

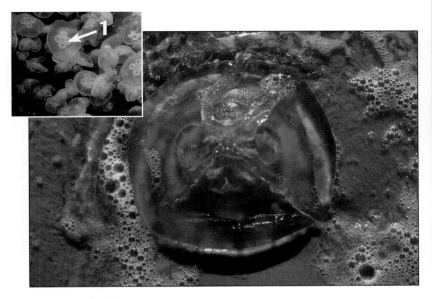

Moon jelly
Aurelia aurita

This delicate jelly with a translucent dome has a margin of short tentacles, like a fringe. In the centre of the dome are four horseshoe-shaped gonads (1) that are more opaque, usually of a whitish or pinkish colour. The moon jelly can reach 25 to 30 cm in diameter.

DISTRIBUTION:
From Greenland and the Gulf of St. Lawrence to the Caribbean.

HABITAT:
At the surface of the water, sometimes washed up onto the beach.

The moon jelly is very common in bays and ports during the summer months. The moon jelly is only slightly venomous. In some people, touching them can cause a prickly or mild burning sensation. It can be found in large numbers where plankton is abundant. This jelly traps its food using the fringe of its sticky tentacles, which are then 'licked' clean by the mouth parts in the middle.

Northern red anemone
Tealia felina, Urticina felina

A strikingly beautiful anemone with a smooth column, the northern red anemone attaches to rocks using a sticky disk on its underside. The tentacles (1) are like short fingers with rounded ends. The column is red, purple, or brownish red, often striated with green or white. It can reach 7.5 cm in height—even more when living at greater depths.

DISTRIBUTION:
From south of the Arctic to Casco Bay, Maine.

HABITAT:
Intertidal and subtidal zones.

The northern red anemone is capable of totally retracting itself when disturbed. We then only see the flattened column (2) on the rock, with a small opening in the centre. In order to feed, the anemone extends its tentacles, capturing small fish or invertebrates that pass close by. The tentacles have microscopic stinging cells that grab prey and bring it to the mouth, located in the centre of the anemone.

Silver-spotted anemone
Bunodactis stella

The silver-spotted anemone is a small, delicate creature with a translucent column and thin tentacles forming a pale ring in the middle and, often, a whitish spot at the base. White lines around the diameter of the mouth region are frequently observed. The colour of the column and the tentacles varies from pale or dark olive green to blue green, sometimes pinkish. It can be up to 3.5 cm long and 5 cm wide.

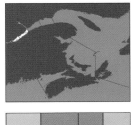

DISTRIBUTION:
Lower Estuary and the Gulf of St. Lawrence, and from Nova Scotia to Maine.

HABITAT:
Lower intertidal zone, tidal pools, and shallow subtidal zones.

This anemone attaches to rocks and is often buried in the sand in tidal pools, leaving just the tentacles exposed.

Lion's mane jelly
Cyanea capillata

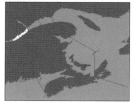

A colourful jelly that can be very large, the lion's mane has a wide bell with multiple mouth parts and relatively long tentacles (1). Its diameter can be as large as 2 metres across, and the tentacles can extend as much as 60 metres!

Inside the bell, the organs can vary in colour depending on the jelly's age and geographical location, ranging from pink or yellow, to darker brown, orange, or red. In recent years, blue-purple specimens (2) have been observed along our coast. Initially thought to be bluefire jellies from western Europe, they were determined to be lion's mane jellies, but may turn out to be a different species.

DISTRIBUTION:
From the Arctic to the Gulf of Mexico.

HABITAT:
Mostly subtidal, in bays and estuaries and at the surface of the ocean, but can wash up on shore.

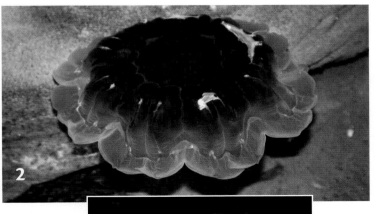

2

Some lion's manes have been found measuring 2.4 metres across, making this the largest species of jelly in the world. Interestingly, it feeds on other jellies, such as the moon jelly, and other planktonic animals. Some species of fish may hide under the bell for protection.

The lion's mane has a powerful sting, which can cause severe burns and a painful rash, even after its death. If these jellies wash up on the beach, care should be taken. In our region, they are mostly observed in the spring and summer months, with a few larger specimens lingering into the fall.

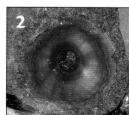

Frilled anemone
Metridium senile

This smooth-columned anemone has up to 1,000 very fine tentacles resembling duvet feathers (1). It attaches to rocks and wharves using a sticky disk. The column has a uniform yellow-brown or orange colour. Occasionally, it is whitish or pinkish. The tentacles are sometimes paler, almost white. The anemone can grow to 10 cm high and 7.5 cm wide.

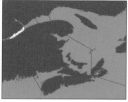

DISTRIBUTION:
From the Arctic to Delaware Bay, and the lower estuary to the Gulf of St. Lawrence.

HABITAT:
Intertidal and subtidal zones.

Unlike the other anemones in this book, the frilled anemone filters water through its fine tentacles in order to capture plankton as food. At the slightest touch, the anemone totally retracts (2).

Ctenophora

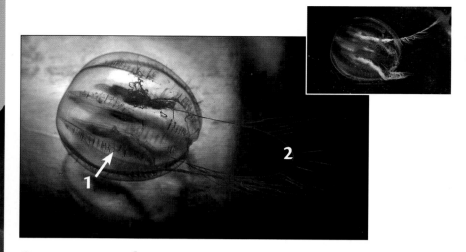

Sea gooseberry
Pleurobrachia pileus

With a small, transparent, egg-shaped but firm body, the sea gooseberry is hard to see underwater. With a hand-lens, it is possible to see 8 rows of iridescent comb plates (1) along almost the entire body. It has 2 long contractile tentacles (2) that are fringed on one side. Sometimes, the orange- or pink-coloured organs can be seen through its body. It can reach 28 mm in length.

DISTRIBUTION:
Bay of Fundy to Florida.

HABITAT:
Swarms in inshore waters along the coast in winter. Mostly subtidal.

Sea gooseberries are known to be very voracious, eating large quantities of smaller animals, including fish larva and zooplankton. Its prey is caught by the sticky tentacles. But, unlike many jellies, they do not sting. In winter, they can be observed in large numbers off wharves and along the shore, sometimes ending up on beaches at low tide.

Mollusca

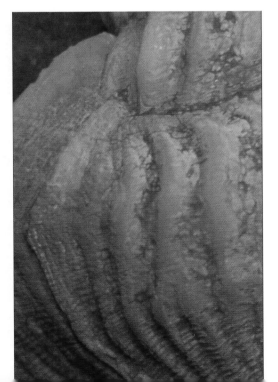

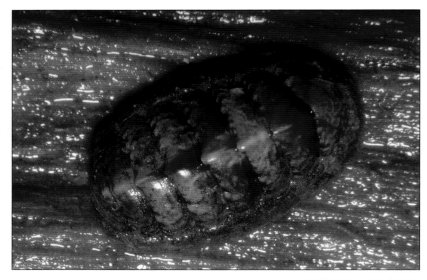

Red chiton
Ischnochiton ruber,
Tonicella rubra

This small mollusk has a shell formed by 8 dorsal plates, with a thick girdle all around the edge, which helps create a strong hold on rocks. It is reddish, sometimes with white and brown markings. It never grows beyond 2.5 cm long.

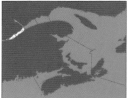

DISTRIBUTION:
From the Arctic to Massachusetts, and the lower estuary to the Gulf of St. Lawrence.

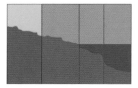

HABITAT:
Intertidal and subtidal zones.

The red chiton is an important herbivore in marine ecosystems, grazing on coralline algae and other seaweed. It uses its large foot under its shell to move around, but when it feels threatened, it lowers its whole shell down to clamp itself tightly to the surface of rocks, making it impossible for predators to dislodge it. If it is taken off the rocks, it rolls up in a ball to protect its soft body.

Tortoiseshell limpet
Acmaea testudinalis, Tectura testudinalis

An attractive mollusk with a smooth shell, the tortoiseshell limpet has a flattened cone shape, with several lines and geometric markings. It is white with different shades of brown. The inside of the shell is white with one brown "stain." It is usually around 3 cm long, but can occasionally reach 5 cm.

DISTRIBUTION:
The Arctic to Connecticut, in the Saguenay Fjord, and from the upper estuary (downriver) to the Gulf of St. Lawrence.

HABITAT:
Lower intertidal to the shallow subtidal zone.

The tortoiseshell limpet is able to hold on to hard surfaces with such strength that it is often impossible to dislodge it. This species is an important grazer of seaweeds.

Common northern lacuna, Chink shell
Lacuna vincta

The common northern lacuna is a tiny gastropod that looks very much like a periwinkle, but with a more elongated spire and a thinner, almost translucent shell. It has an umbilicus (1) shaped like a narrow slit next to the aperture. The shell is smooth, brown or yellow in colour, often with paler or darker spiral bands. It can be up to 1.2 cm long.

DISTRIBUTION:
The Arctic to New Jersey, and from the upper estuary (upriver) to the Gulf of St. Lawrence.

HABITAT:
Intertidal and subtidal zones.

Lacuna are often found among kelp, especially near their base.

Common periwinkle, Edible periwinkle
Littorina littorea

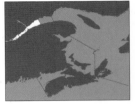

This small common gastropod often has spiral stripes and a shell with a conic shape and a short spire. It is brown or dark grey, with a whitish inner lip. The outer lip does not rejoin the shell at an angle (1). Its length can reach 4 cm.

DISTRIBUTION:
Labrador to New Jersey, including the lower estuary (downriver) and the Gulf of St. Lawrence.

HABITAT:
Intertidal zone, especially in the lower part.

This periwinkle is the most commonly found species on the region's beaches, on rocks, and on wooden structures. In terms of edibility, it is popular in Europe, where it is used in seafood recipes.

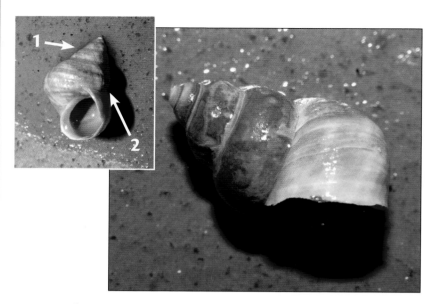

Rough periwinkle
Littorina saxatilis

The rough periwinkle, a small gastropod, is very similar to the common periwinkle, and has a somewhat taller spire (1), often with thin spiral ribs. It is also smaller overall. The outer lip rejoins the shell almost at a right angle (2). The shell is brown, black, or white, and either with or without yellow stains. Most specimens measure less than 1.2 cm.

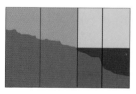

DISTRIBUTION:
The Arctic to New Jersey, and from the upper estuary (upriver) to the Gulf of St. Lawrence.

HABITAT:
Intertidal zone, including the upper part.

The rough periwinkle can survive several days out of the water, and tolerates lower salinity levels. It likes to graze on seaweed.

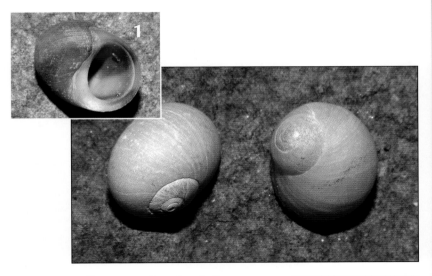

Smooth periwinkle, Northern yellow periwinkle
Littorina obtusata

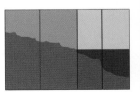

A small round gastropod with a flattened spire, the smooth periwinkle has a very smooth shell, just like the northern moon snail, but without the umbilicus. Its colour varies greatly: brown, olive green, red, yellow, orange, grey, black, or sometimes striped (1). It can reach 1.3 cm long.

DISTRIBUTION:
The Arctic to New Jersey. In the Saguenay Fjord, and from the upper estuary (upriver) to the Gulf of St. Lawrence.

HABITAT:
Intertidal zone.

The smooth periwinkle is often found hidden among brown seaweed (*Fucus sp.*), but it prefers grazing on microscopic algae.

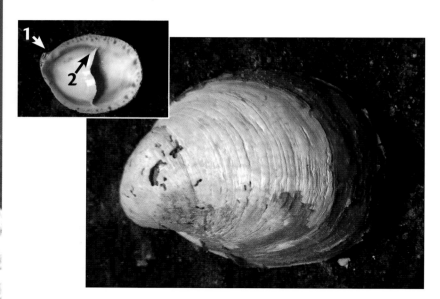

Common Atlantic slipper shell
Crepidula fornicata

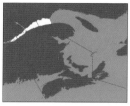

This mollusk has a dome-shaped shell with an apex that curves to one side (1). In the concave interior of the shell, there is a calcareous platform (2) that covers half of the opening. The shell is pale grey, beige, or reddish-brown, often with darker stains and lines. The inside of the shell can be white, yellowish, or purplish. It can reach 4 cm in length.

DISTRIBUTION:
The Gulf of St. Lawrence to Florida.

HABITAT:
Lower intertidal and shallow subtidal zone.

Slipper shells live in calm shallow waters, attached to any solid surface, including other slipper shells. They then form a stack of several individuals.

Cup-and-saucer limpet
Crucibulum striatum

The cup-and-saucer limpet is a mollusk that has a conic-shaped shell with an apex turned to one side at the very top (1). The surface of the shell shows radial lines. Inside the concave opening is a tongue-shaped calcareous platform (2). The shell can be whitish, yellowish, or pinkish on the outside, whil the inside is whitish with a yellow tinge. It can measure up to 2.5 cm.

DISTRIBUTION:
Nova Scotia and the Bay of Fundy to Florida.

HABITAT:
Lower intertidal and subtidal zone.

This limpet is often visible on rocks and on other shells.

Northern moon snail
Lunatia heros

A large round gastropod, the northern moon snail has a flattened spire (1), a smooth shell, and a round umbilicus forming a hole (2). The shell's aperture is large, and the interior surface is very smooth and glassy (3). This snail is a pale greyish-beige or whitish colour. The inside of the shell is often darker, with purple hues. It can reach 10-12 cm.

Very similar to the northern moon shell, the spotted moon shell (*Lunatia triseriata*) is a much smaller species (4), with a series of purplish to brownish spots. The body is white with black tentacles. It can reach 25 mm in diameter.

DISTRIBUTION:
Labrador to North Carolina, including the lower estuary and the Gulf of St. Lawrence.

HABITAT:
Intertidal and subtidal zone.

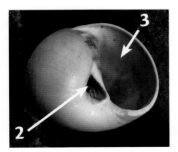

The body of the northern moon snail, with its enormous foot, seems to be too large to fit inside the shell, but it is able to totally retract inside. Mostly living buried just under the sand, it lays its eggs in a gelatinous envelope that forms a collar (5). When found on the beach, this collar feels like a sandy piece of rubber.

This moon snail feeds on other mollusks by drilling a hole (6) in their shell using a radula (raspy tongue), and retreiving the flesh through the hole.

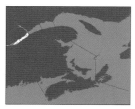

Atlantic dogwinkle, dogwhelk
Thais lapillus, Nucella lapillus

With a shape that varies greatly, this gastropod has a large aperture and many spiral ribs (1) on the surface. On occasion, there are axial ribs as well. An anterior canal (2) for the siphon is present at the bottom of the aperture. The colour also varies, but is usually brown, orange, yellow, or white. The interior of the shell is whitish with a brownish-purple tinge. This shell can grow to be 4 cm long.

DISTRIBUTION:
The Arctic to Long Island Sound, including the lower estuary and the Gulf of St. Lawrence.

HABITAT:
Mostly in the intertidal, but sometimes in the shallow subtidal zone.

The Atlantic dogwinkle lives in rocky habitats in the intertidal zones, hiding among brown seaweed and squeezed into rock crevices. It feeds in a similar way to the northern moon snail, by drilling a hole into the shell of blue mussels to extract the flesh. It will also eat barnacles.

Eastern mud snail, Eroded basket shell
Nassarius obsoletus

The eastern mud snail is a little stockier than the New England dog whelk, and often has an eroded apex. The texture of the shell surface forms a series of spiral striations and pearls, while the columella has a fold near the base of the aperture. The shell is dark brown, almost black. The aperture is also dark brown, with a shiny, dark inner lip. The shell can grow up to 3 cm.

DISTRIBUTION:
From the Gulf of St. Lawrence (Bay of Chaleur) to Florida.

HABITAT:
Intertidal and shallow subtidal zone.

The eastern mud snail prefers to bury itself in muddy substrates. That is why we often find it covered in mud and seaweed. It will occasionally feed on dead animal carcasses.

American pelican's foot, Duck's foot shell
Aporrhais occidentalis

The striking feature on individuals which measure 4 cm or more is the greatly extended outer lip that forms a pointy wing. The shell also has a tall spire, and the surface has axial ribs and smaller spiral lines. It is pale brown or pale grey. The interior of the aperture is shiny and white. Its length can be up to 7 cm.

DISTRIBUTION:
The Arctic to North Carolina, and in the lower estuary and Gulf of St. Lawrence.

HABITAT:
In the subtidal zone but sometimes on the beach.

Instead of gliding with its foot in order to move around like most other gastropods, the American pelican's foot takes "leaps," by balancing itself on the outer lip and putting down its foot a few millimetres further. Even though it lives mainly below the low-tide level, we sometimes find beached individuals.

New England dog whelk, New England basket whelk
Nassarius trivittatus

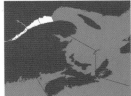

This gastropod has a tall spire and a thin outer lip. The exterior is pearled, forming a raised, checkered pattern. The shell is grey, brown, and yellow, with darker lines. The inner lip is whitish and shiny. It can grow up to 2 cm long.

DISTRIBUTION:
The Gulf of the St. Lawrence to Florida.

HABITAT:
In the subtidal, mostly shallow zone.

The New England dog whelk prefers calm waters with a sandy substrate. It is the most common *Nassarius* species on the Atlantic coast.

Stimpson's whelk
Colus stimpsoni

This gastropod's aperture is half of its shell's overall length. The spire is tall, and there is an anterior canal at the base of the aperture. The shell is dark brown, but can exhibit paler spots as it wears out. It also has small spiral lines on the surface. It can reach 12.5 cm.

DISTRIBUTION:
From Labrador to North Carolina, and in the Gulf of St. Lawrence.

HABITAT:
Mostly in the subtidal zone.

The Stimpson's whelk can sometimes be seen in the lower intertidal zone, but mostly in tidal pools. In the subtidal zone, it prefers sandy and rocky bottoms.

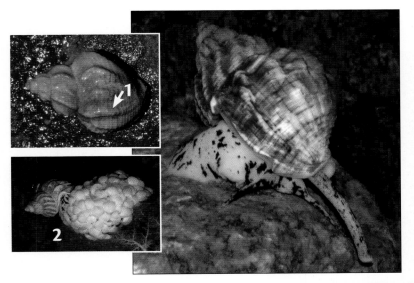

Waved whelk
Buccinum undatum

The waved whelk is taller than it is wide, with prominent axial ribs (1) and smaller spiral cords. The gastropod's aperture is large, with a pale interior surface, and an anterior canal for the siphon at the base. The shell is greyish-yellow or whitish in colour, while the animal's body is white with black spots. It rarely reaches 10 cm in length.

DISTRIBUTION:
The Arctic to New Jersey, including the Saguenay Fjord, and from the upper estuary (downriver) to the Gulf of St. Lawrence.

HABITAT:
In the subtidal zone and in tidal pools.

The empty shells of the waved whelk are often used by hermit crabs as 'mobile homes.' Large "mounds" of eggs can sometimes be seen attached to rocks in tide pools (2). Young whelks live mostly in tidal pools of the intertidal zone, and the adults are mostly in the subtidal zone.

Ten-ridged whelk
Neptunea decemcostata

A robust gastropod, the ten-ridged whelk has 7 to 10 prominent spiral cords (1) on the surface of the shell. It can be reddish- or greyish-brown, and can reach 10 cm in length.

DISTRIBUTION:
Nova Scotia to Cape Cod.

HABITAT:
The subtidal zone.

The ten-ridged whelk is the only member of the whelk family considered to be venomous. It transfers a neurotoxic substance into its prey to cause paralysis. However, it is not dangerous to humans. Fishermen often find this whelk in their lobster traps.

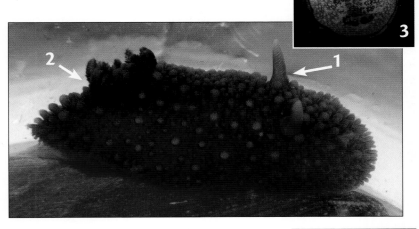

Rough-mantled nudibranch
Onchidoris bilamellata

This is a simple, oval-shaped mollusk without a shell. The surface of its body is covered with little round bumps. The body is firm compared to other sea slugs. There is a pair of tentacles (1) at the front, on top of the head, and a ring of feathery gills (2) at the back. The body pattern is a combination of dark brown, creamy white, or beige markings and spots. It can reach 3 cm.

DISTRIBUTION:
The Bay of Fundy to Rhode Island.

HABITAT:
The intertidal zone.

The rough-mantled nudibranch climbs on top of rocks in the intertidal zone. If its tentacles or gills are touched, they instantly retract completely inside the body (3).

Bushy-backed nudibranch
Dendronotus frondosus

A mollusk without a shell, the bush-backed nudibranch has feather-like growths (cerata) on its back. The body is soft, and either brownish or reddish with tiny white or rust-coloured spots. It can attain a length of up to 8 cm.

DISTRIBUTION:
The Arctic to New Jersey, in the Saguenay Fjord and from the upper estuary (downriver) to the Gulf of St. Lawrence.

HABITAT:
Lower intertidal to the shallow subtidal zone. Also in tidal pools.

The bushy-backed nudibranch is often seen on submerged objects and among seaweed. When out of water, its body becomes a gelatinous blob. Once back in the water, the sea slug takes shape again and extends the cerata on its back.

Red-gilled nudibranch
Coryphella sp.

These elegant little shell-less mollusks have up to 100 finger-shaped tentacles on each side of their back. There are 2 pairs of antennae at the front of the soft body. They are translucent, creamy white. The tips of the tentacles are opaque white, and red at the centre. They can grow up to 3 cm long.

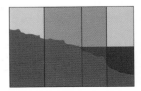

DISTRIBUTION:
The Arctic to south of Cape Cod.

HABITAT:
The lower intertidal to the deep subtidal zone.

The red-gilled nudibranch likes to hide among hydroids, as they are an important source of food. That is why we often see them along floating docks.

Maned nudibranch
Aeolidia papillosa

This shell-less mollusk can have up to 400 finger-shaped tentacles on each side of the back. There are 2 pairs of antennae at the front of the soft body. It can be brown, pinkish, or greyish; sometimes very pale. It can reach up to 10 cm.

DISTRIBUTION:
The Bay of Fundy to Cape Cod.

HABITAT:
In tidal pools and in shallow subtidal zones.

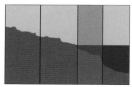

The maned nudibranch feeds mostly on frilled anemones, the tiny stinging cells of which find their way into the tentacles of the sea slug. After being digested, they are used by the nudibranch as a defense mechanism.

Blue mussel
Mytilus edulis

The ubiquitous blue mussel bivalve has a smooth shell and a hinge that forms a pointy beak (umbo), with a few fine teeth below. The valves are blackish or brownish, often with blueish or whitish parts once the dark layer wears off. The inside of the shell is purplish. They can reach 10 cm.

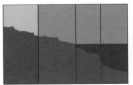

DISTRIBUTION:
The Arctic to South Carolina, including the Saguenay Fjord, and from the upper estuary (upriver) to the Gulf of St. Lawrence.

HABITAT:
Lower intertidal and subtidal zone.

The blue mussel lives mostly in shoals, with several individuals attached together and to the rocks using very strong threads (1). There is much competition between mussels, barnacles, and seaweed to establish themselves on solid objects in the intertidal zone. The blue mussel filters large volumes of water to feed, and tolerates water that is somewhat brackish. This edible mussel is the most recognized one in the market.

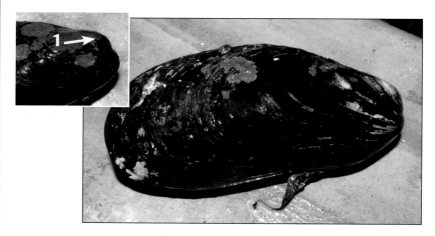

Horse mussel, Northern horse mussel
Modiolus modiolus

While very much like the blue mussel, the horse mussel is often larger, and has an umbo that does not directly line up with the beak (hinge) (1). There are no teeth below the hinge. Both valves are blackish or brownish, often with whitish parts (sometimes stained with purple) once the dark layer wears off. The interior of the shell is whitish. Its length can reach 15 cm.

DISTRIBUTION:
The Arctic to Long Island Sound (rare further south), including the Saguenay Fjord, and from the upper estuary (downriver) to the Gulf of St. Lawrence.

HABITAT:
The subtidal, and occasionally the lower intertidal zone.

The horse mussel tends to live in deeper waters than the blue mussel. Seastars and lobsters often love to eat them. Young horse mussels are more bluish than brownish. Although usually found in the subtidal zone, they can sometimes be in the lower intertidal zone in the north. Its empty shell is most commonly found on the beach.

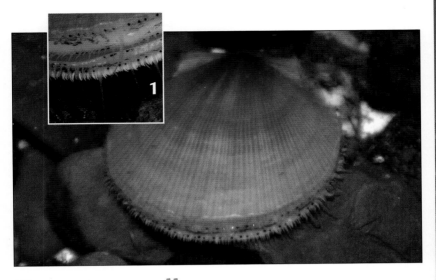

1

Deep-sea scallop
Placopecten magellanicus

This bivalve, with a smooth, flattened shell, has fine lines on the surface, radiating out from the hinge. A series of very small black eyes can be seen all around the lips (1). The valves' colour can vary from whitish to brownish or orange. Quite often, the bottom valve is paler. It can reach 20 cm long.

DISTRIBUTION:
Labrador to Cape Cod.

HABITAT:
Mostly in the subtidal zone.

The scallop is the only bivalve that can "swim" over short distances. It does so by abruptly opening and closing its valves. Water is expelled towards the back, on each side of the hinge, and the scallop moves forward. Out of the water, it often "spits" the water out of its valves. This is an edible species; the part that is consumed being the round muscle that joins both valves. Its empty valves are regularly found on the beach.

Eastern oyster, American oyster, Virginian oyster, Common oyster
Crassostrea virginica

With many common names, this strange bivalve has an irregularly shaped shell with a rough surface full of folds. The top valve is more flattened than the bottom, which is often moored on hard surfaces. The exterior of the shell is more or less dark grey. Inside, the shell is whitish with a round stain (1) tinged with brownish-purple. It can be up to 30 cm long.

DISTRIBUTION:
The Gulf of St. Lawrence (Caraquet Bay, NB, the Magdalen Islands, QC), and from Maine to Mexico.

HABITAT:
From the intertidal to the shallow subtidal zone.

The eastern oyster prefers brackish water and lives in shoals inside river estuaries. It is cultivated and sometimes harvested for commercial purposes all along the American east coast. In the Gulf of St. Lawrence, it is limited to the southern parts, in shallow bays, as it requires higher temperatures during the summer months in order to reproduce.

Black clam, Ocean quahog, Mahogany clam

Arctica islandica

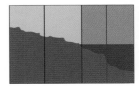

A robust bivalve with a thick, round shell, the black clam has a bulging umbo slightly turned to one side (1). There is no pallial sinus. It is brownish-yellow (young specimens) to brownish-black, with whitish parts where worn. The interior of the shell is whitish. Individuals can reach 12 cm in length.

DISTRIBUTION:
The Arctic to North Carolina, and in the lower estuary and Gulf of St. Lawrence.

HABITAT:
The subtidal zone.

The black clam can live a very long time, sometimes up to 100 years. Its empty shell can often be found on the beach.

Waved astarte
Astarte undata

This bivalve has a triangular-shaped shell, slightly flattened and rounded, with several prominent concentric ribs on the surface. There is no pallial sinus inside the shell. There are fine teeth (1) on the valves' inner margin. The exterior of the shell is yellowish- or dark brown, while the interior is whitish. It can be up to 3.5 cm.

DISTRIBUTION:
Labrador to New Jersey.

HABITAT:
The subtidal zone.

The waved astarte feeds mainly on marine plankton. Though it lives mostly in the subtidal zone, it can sometimes be found on the beach.

Northern cardita, Northern heart shell
Cyclocardia borealis

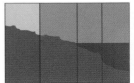

The thick shell of this small bivalve has an undulated surface with rough, prominent radial ribs. The valves have a rounded triangular shape, with an umbo slightly turned to one side (1). There is no pallial sinus inside the shell. It is greyish brown or dark brown with whitish parts where worn. The interior is whitish. It can reach 3.8 cm.

DISTRIBUTION:
Labrador to New Jersey.

HABITAT:
Mostly in the subtidal, but occasionally in the lower intertidal zone.

This cardita lives on sandy or pebbly substrates, and between rocks. It is sometimes found on beaches after storms.

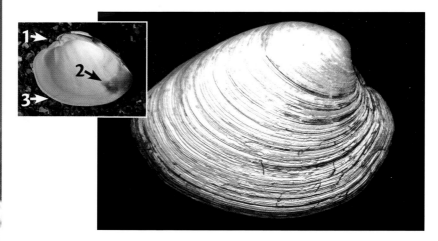

Northern quahog, Bay quahog, Hard clam
Mercenaria mercenaria

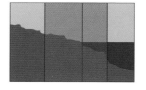

This bivalve is an oval and triangular shape, with concentric ridges that become smoother in adults. The umbo is bulging and turns slightly to one side (1). When both valves are closed, a lunule is seen under the umbo when viewed from the side. There is a small pallial sinus (2) shaped like a "V," and fine teeth (3) on the valves' inner margin. The shell's exterior is whitish or greyish, while the interior is white with a purple stain. The shell's length can be up to 15 cm.

DISTRIBUTION:
Around the Magdalen Islands, QC; Miramichi Bay, NB; towards the east in the Gulf of St. Lawrence, including the western coast of Newfoundland; and from Maine to the Gulf of Mexico.

HABITAT:
Intertidal and shallow subtidal zone.

The northern quahog buries itself in the sediments of shallow bays, which warm up quickly during summer months. It is often harvested in the southern parts of the Gulf of St. Lawrence.

False quahog
Pitar morrhuana,
Pitar morrhuanus

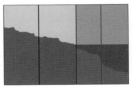

This bivalve resembles the Northern quahog, it has a smooth inner margin, without teeth. When the valves are closed, a lunule is visible under the umbo when viewed from the side. Inside the shell, there is a pallial sinus shaped like a "V" (1), and three teeth just under the umbo (2). The exterior of the shell is chalky white, tinged with a grey, orange, or rust colour. The interior is white. It can reach 5 cm.

DISTRIBUTION:
The Bay of Chaleur, NB, to North Carolina, including Prince Edward Island.

HABITAT:
The subtidal zone.

Like most other bivalves, the false quahog filters seawater to feed on plankton. It prefers sandy bottoms.

Atlantic surf clam, Bar clam
Spisula solidissima

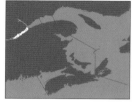

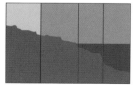

A bivalve with an oval or triangular shape, this clam has a bulging umbo (1), which is more centred than that of the northern quahog. Inside the shell, along the lateral teeth on each side of the umbo, are very fine striations (2). The pallial sinus is small (3), extending slightly past the muscle scar. The shell exterior is relatively smooth, tinged with olive brown or yellow. It can be up to 20 cm long.

DISTRIBUTION:
Labrador to South Carolina, and the lower estuary and Gulf of St. Lawrence.

HABITAT:
Lower intertidal to the subtidal zone.

The Atlantic surf clam is one of the region's largest bivalves. It feeds on plankton and small organic detritus. At 3 or 4 years of age, it reaches commercial market size.

Arctic wedge clam
Mesodesma arctatum

An oval-shaped bivalve, the Arctic wedge clam has an off-centre umbo (1). The lateral teeth have fine striations on both sides. There is a chondrophore (2) on each valve, just under the umbo. The shell is whitish, tinged with yellow or grey, and has concentric lines on the surface. The interior is whitish. It can reach 4 cm.

DISTRIBUTION:
The Saguenay Fjord, from the upper estuary (upriver) to the Gulf of St. Lawrence, to Virginia.

HABITAT:
Lower intertidal and shallow subtidal zone.

This bivalve filters water to feed on plankton. It lives mostly in shallow waters, over a sandy bottom.

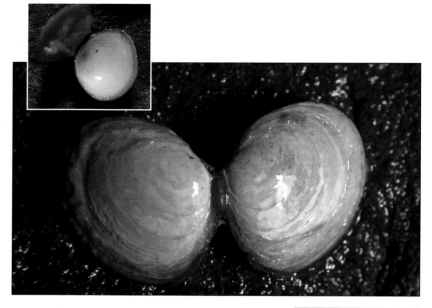

Little macoma clam, Baltic clam

Macoma sp.

This small bivalve, with a flattened, oval triangular shape, is not quite symmetrical, and has a thin and chalky shell. The different-sized pallial sinuses merge with the pallial lines either completely or partially. The shell is whitish, tinged with pale greyish-brown or pink. It can measure up to 5 cm.

DISTRIBUTION:
The Arctic to Georgia, in the Saguenay Fjord, and from the upper estuary (upriver) to the Gulf of St. Lawrence.

HABITAT:
Intertidal and shallow subtidal zone.

The macomas enjoy calm bays, buried in mud rich in organic matter. They can tolerate brackish waters.

Common razor clam, Atlantic jackknife clam
Ensis directus

This strange-looking bivalve is much longer than it is wide, with a slightly curved knife shape. It has a thin, fragile shell. The exterior is smooth, brown olive in colour, with whitish parts where worn. The interior is whitish and sometimes tinged with purple. It can reach up to 25 cm.

DISTRIBUTION:
Labrador to Georgia, and in the lower estuary and Gulf of St. Lawrence.

HABITAT:
From the lower intertidal to the subtidal zone.

The common razor clam lives mostly over sandy or muddy substrates, where it buries itself using its long foot. With a short siphon, it spends most of its time close to the surface, but if it feels threatened, it uses its long foot to reach the bottom of its burrow, which can be as much as 50 cm below the surface.

Soft-shelled clam, Common soft-shelled clam, Steamer clam

Mya arenaria

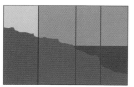

A bivalve with an elongated oval shape, this clam has a shell with small concentric ridges. There is a chondrophore (1) shaped like a spoon on the hinge of one of the valves. The exterior of the shell is whitish, occasionally tinged with grey or beige. The interior is whitish, with a large pallial sinus (2) that covers close to half of the width of the shell. This clam rarely reaches 15 cm.

DISTRIBUTION:
The Arctic to North Carolina (Cape Hatteras), in the Saguenay Fjord, and from the upper estuary (upriver) to the Gulf of St. Lawrence.

HABITAT:
From the intertidal to the subtidal zone.

The soft-shelled clam buries into sand in bays and estuaries. It uses two siphons (3) to filter water, in order to get oxygen and plankton. When the siphons are retracted, all that is visible is a hole at the surface of the sand. It is often eaten fried.

Truncate soft-shell clam
Mya truncata

This bivalve is very much like the soft-shelled clam; however, it has a truncated end that stays wide open (1), a large pallial sinus (2) shaped like a U, and a spoon-shaped chondrophore, which is smaller than the soft-shelled clam's. It varies from olive brown to yellowish-brown, with whitish parts where worn. The interior is whitish. It can reach 7.5 cm.

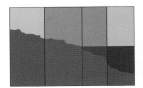

DISTRIBUTION:
The Arctic to Cape Cod, in the Saguenay Fjord, and in the lower estuary and Gulf of St. Lawrence.

HABITAT:
From the lower intertidal to the subtidal zone.

This is one of the edible clams. It lives buried in sand and filters water to eat small bits of organic matter.

Squid eggs

This egg mass is composed of long, translucent, gelatinous fingers full of small, opaque white spots. It can be found holding on to seaweed clumps or rocks, and can have hundreds of fingers; each can measure up to 15 cm long.

DISTRIBUTION:
The Arctic to Cape Cod, and in deeper waters further south.

HABITAT:
Along beaches, near the low tide level.

Two species of squid (which are part of the cephalopod family, including octopus) visit our region. The most common is the short-finned or boreal squid (*Illex illecebrosus*). It lays small floating egg masses of 1mm in size. The other species is the long-finned squid (*Loligo pealei*), shown in the image above. The hundreds of tiny squid develop inside and hatch after about 30 days. The young squid, with orange and black spots (1) are so small that they drift with the currents. It takes a good hand-lens to observe them.

Arthropoda

Anemone sea spider
Pycnogonum littorale

A tiny animal, the sea spider is not really related to true spiders. It does share a similar shape, with eight legs. The body, which can be light brown or beige, is divided into four main plates, each supporting a pair of legs. The cone at the front of the sea spider (1) is its proboscis (nose). The sea spider can measure 5 to 10 mm in length.

DISTRIBUTION:
From the Gulf of St. Lawrence to Long Island Sound.

HABITAT:
In the lower intertidal and shallow subtidal zones.

Just like the name suggests, the anemone sea spider can often be found clinging to anemones. It feeds on them, using its proboscis to dig into the base of the anemones, and then sucking out their soft tissue.

Northern rock barnacle, common rock barnacle, Northern acorn barnacle

Balanus balanoides, Semibalanus balanoides

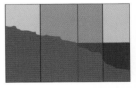

This pyramid-shaped shell is formed with calcareous plates with slightly prominent ribs. The overall form can vary according to how tightly crammed together the barnacles are in an area. The opening at the top, with its two movable plates, has a lozenge shape (1). The base is non-calcareous. Usually whitish, the barnacle's surface is sometimes brown or green, which is caused by algae. It can grow to 3 cm.

DISTRIBUTION:
The Arctic to Delaware, and from the upper estuary to the Gulf of St. Lawrence.

HABITAT:
Mostly in the lower intertidal zone, but can live in deeper subtidal waters.

This barnacle is very common, and lives just above the blue mussel level in the intertidal zone. It attaches to rocks, wharves, and, even on the shells of other animals including crabs, lobsters, and mollusks. Barnacles feed by opening the two movable plates at the top, and by extending an open "hand" (2) in a rhythmic fashion to capture plankton. This hand is actually their articulated legs.

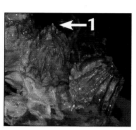

Northern ridged barnacle, Rough barnacle

Balanus balanus

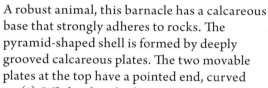

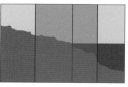

A robust animal, this barnacle has a calcareous base that strongly adheres to rocks. The pyramid-shaped shell is formed by deeply grooved calcareous plates. The two movable plates at the top have a pointed end, curved up (1). While whitish, they can be stained by algae and mud. They can reach 5 cm. There is a similar but smaller species (3 cm) that can be found in the same region; the crenate barnacle (*Balanus crenatus*) has a smooth outer shell made of plates that are pointed at the top.

DISTRIBUTION:
The Arctic to Cape Cod, from the upper estuary to the Gulf of St. Lawrence, and in the Saguenay Fjord.

HABITAT:
Lower intertidal and the deeper subtidal zone.

The northern-ridged barnacle is mostly found in cold deeper waters, but in this region it can live in the lower intertidal zone. Its main predator is the common seastar.

Pelagic goose barnacles

Lepas sp.

This is a very different barnacle compared to the northern rock barnacle. It does not have a calcareous shell around it; instead, it is perched at the end of a dark-purplish rubbery stalk, and the body resembles an ear. Whitish limy plates enclose the animal, and they can be tinted with blue or orange. It can be 15 cm tall.

DISTRIBUTION:
The entire east coast.

HABITAT:
The subtidal zone, but can be found on floating objects washed ashore.

Pelagic goose barnacles are found offshore, but they can be seen attached to floating debris such as buoys, planks, or seaweed near the shore. Just like other barnacles, they have a feathery "hand" that emerges from between the plates to grab plankton from the water in order to feed.

Beach hopper, beach flea
Orchestia sp.

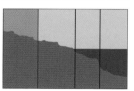

A small nervous semi-terrestrial crustacean, this species looks like a short shrimp. It has round, black eyes (1). The beach hopper varies from reddish-brown to greyish-green. It can reach 2 cm.

DISTRIBUTION:
All along the eastern coast.

HABITAT:
Upper intertidal zone, or just above.

The beach hopper can be found under seaweed masses and debris at low tide, even at the upper level of the beach. It is capable of breathing out of water. When it is disturbed, the beach hopper leaps erratically in all directions, just like a dog or cat flea, but does not bite.

Sideswimmers
Gammarus sp.

These small crustaceans resemble curved shrimps with a stocky body. Their eyes are often shaped like a comma (1). They swim on their sides, in a "nervous" fashion. Sideswimmers are usually dark reddish-brown. Some individuals can be 3 cm long.

DISTRIBUTION:
More common in the north, from the Arctic to New England, including from the upper estuary (upriver) to the Gulf of St. Lawrence, and the Saguenay Fjord.

HABITAT:
In the north, it lives in the intertidal zone, but in the south, it is more often found in the subtidal zone.

On the beach, look under a rock or a seaweed patch to discover many of these swimming in all directions, especially in tidal pools. Sideswimmers are an important food source for many animals living in the intertidal and subtidal zones.

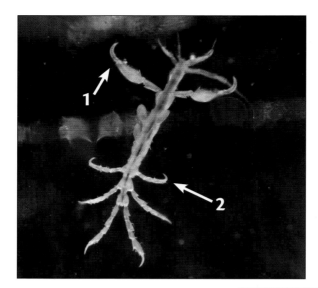

Skeleton shrimp, caprellid amphipod
Caprella sp.

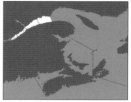

Skeleton shrimps are small, very thin and elongated crustaceans that look and behave very much like a praying mantis. They have small claws (1) resembling hands in prayer. At the base of these shrimps, there are three pairs of pointed legs (2) used to hook on to surfaces. Sometimes translucent, they can also be very

colourful, in the reddish-brown range. Larger specimens can reach 5 cm.

DISTRIBUTION:
The Arctic to North Carolina.

HABITAT:
The subtidal zone.

These shrimps often hold on to rocks, seaweed, boat hulls, sponges, or anything else that is submerged. They swing back and forth gently, folding in half to catch their prey. When on the move, they behave like inchworms. The males brood their young in a ventral pouch.

Bent mysid shrimp, Opposum shrimp, Chameleon shrimp

Praunus flexuosus

A small and delicate crustacean, the bent mysid has a straighter body than the sideswimmers. Its back forms a small angle, which gives it a slight hump (1). The tail (telson) is "V" shaped. The body is rather translucent, with black eyes. It can grow to be 2.5 to 3 cm long.

DISTRIBUTION:
The upper estuary (downriver) to the Gulf of St. Lawrence, in the Saguenay Fjord, and Nova Scotia to Cape Cod.

HABITAT:
Shallow subtidal zone.

Bent mysids travel in schools, all swimming in the same direction, but if a predator comes after them—such as a fish or whale—they scatter very rapidly to avoid being caught. They are found along wharves, bays, and beaches.

Sand shrimp
Crangon septemspinosa

This is a very inconspicuous shrimp, with a straight body, slightly flattened. It has a short nose (rostrum), and incomplete claws on the first pair of legs in the front. Its colour changes according to the substrate it lives on; from almost transparent, it can become brown, more or less dark grey, and often marbled or mottled. It can reach up to 7 cm in length (males are smaller). A similar species, the red sand shrimp (*Sclerocrangon boreas*) (1) is marbled with red, and has 3 to 4 dorsal spines.

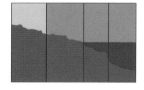

DISTRIBUTION:
The Arctic to Florida, from the upper estuary (upriver) to the Gulf of St. Lawrence, and in the Saguenay Fjord.

HABITAT:
The lower intertidal to the subtidal zone.

The sand shrimp is a master at camouflage. It hides in sand or mud, taking on the same colour as the background. Once settled, it remains still, but if it is disturbed it will suddenly swim to find a new hiding spot.

Hairy hermit crab
Pagurus arcuatus

This crab is very similar to the Acadian hermit crab but it is very "hairy" (fine spines). The smaller of the claws has a ridge of prominent spines. It is dark brown, sometimes paler, and its legs are often striped. The crab's carapace can measure up to 3 cm. The size of the mollusk shell varies with the size of the crab. Another species can be found in our region (*Pagurus pubescens*) but is a lot less hairy.

DISTRIBUTION:
The Arctic to North Carolina, including the Saguenay Fjord, and from the upper estuary (downriver) to the Gulf of St. Lawrence.

HABITAT:
Mostly in the subtidal zone, but sometimes in tidal pools.

Like all hermit crabs, the hairy hermit crab has to find itself a new empty gastropod shell that will fit when it grows bigger. Sometimes there is a type of "fur" covering the surface of the hermit crab's shell (1); this is a hydroid species, tiny cnidarians living in colonies. When the crab leaves the shell, the hydroids disappear.

American lobster
Homarus americanus

There are many different kinds of lobster, but this familiar crustacean is the only species in our region. The majority of them have a pair of claws: a larger, stockier crusher claw with big "teeth," and a more slender pincer claw with sawtooth edges. Two other pairs of legs in the front have smaller claws. Under the tail (abdomen) are several pairs of pleopods shaped like soft paddles. Usually a dark colour, the lobster has olive green, reddish-brown, and orange hues, with blueish joints. On occasion, it can be a rare colour (1) such as blue, yellow, red, and even white. It can reach 1 m in length, and can weigh up to 20 kg.

DISTRIBUTION:
Labrador to Virginia, including the southern part of the Gulf of St. Lawrence.

HABITAT:
Mostly in the subtidal zone.

When lobsters are born they are so small (2) that they become part of the ocean plankton. Once they are 3 to 12 weeks old (3), they find shelter at the bottom of the sea along the coast. They then start a benthic life by feeding on mollusks, fish, crabs, and other crustaceans. Some lobsters can hatch with a body that is a different colour on each side, split right down the middle; these are very rare. The American lobster can live in shallow waters during the summer months, and in deeper waters the rest of the year.

Acadian hermit crab
Pagurus acadianus

The Acadian hermit is a colourful crab that lives in empty gastropod shells. Its claws of similar size are the first pair of legs. Only two other pairs are used for walking. The rest of the body and the last two pairs of legs (1) are concealed inside the shell. There are small bumps and an orange-brown band on the claws' surface. The carapace is often orange with paler edges, and a blueish-grey back. The carapace can reach 3 cm. The size of the gastropod shell varies with the size of the crab.

DISTRIBUTION:
The Gulf of St. Lawrence to Chesapeake Bay.

HABITAT:
Mostly in the subtidal zone, but sometimes in tidal pools.

When the hermit crab grows bigger, it starts looking for a new empty shell that will fit. It then molts and moves into its new home. It can also fight another crab if a suitable shell is already occupied. We run the risk of hurting the crab if we try to dislodge it, as its back legs hold on very strongly to the back of the shell.

Toad crab
Hyas araneus

This crab is longer than it is wide, with a triangular-shaped carapace. It has little bumps on its back and sides, and a triangular nose (rostrum), which is split in half. The legs are usually hairy. Small, slender claws are located on the first pair of legs. It is brownish-beige or olive brown, and can reach 9.5 cm.

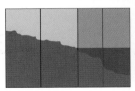

DISTRIBUTION:
The Arctic to Rhode Island, including the Saguenay Fjord, the lower estuary, and the Gulf of St. Lawrence.

HABITAT:
Usually in the subtidal zone, but sometimes in tidal pools.

The shape of the toad crab's carapace, viewed from above, resembles the shape of a toad, hence its name. However, with its many long legs, people often call it a spider crab. It can live in places where we find sand, rocks, and gravel.

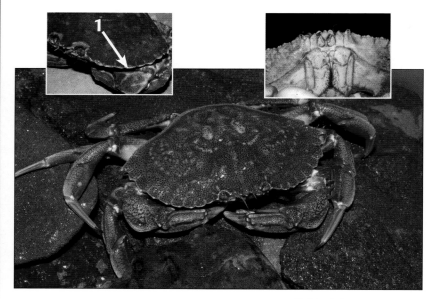

Rock crab
Cancer irroratus

A large crab that is wider than long, it has nine teeth (1) more or less rounded on the edge of its carapace, between the eyes and legs. Also, there are two stocky claws on the first pair of legs at the front. The carapace is yellowish, mottled with brownish-purple markings. They can be up to 14 cm wide.

DISTRIBUTION:
Labrador to South Carolina, including from the upper estuary (upriver) to the Gulf of St. Lawrence.

HABITAT:
The intertidal zone and in tidal pools. Also in the shallow subtidal zone.

This crab has a strong set of claws to crush mollusks, urchins, and seastars. It likes to hide between rocks at low tide but can also bury in mud. A small commercial fishery exists for the rock crab.

Green crab, European green crab
Carcinus maenas

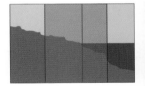

The carapace of this very active crab is slightly wider than it is long. There are five pointed teeth (1) on the edge of the carapace between the eyes and the legs. The two back legs are slightly flattened. There are stocky claws on the first pair of legs in the front. Usually green, it is sometimes marbled with black, yellow, or greyish-blue markings. The underside is sometimes reddish-orange. It can be up to 7.5 cm wide.

DISTRIBUTION:
The Gulf of St. Lawrence around Prince Edward Island, and from Nova Scotia and the Bay of Fundy to New Jersey.

HABITAT:
The intertidal and shallow subtidal zone.

This European species was accidentally introduced to the east coast of New England, and it continues to expand its range north and south. It has a tendency to become very common and to displace the native species of crab. The green crab can live in salt- or brackish water, between rocks and under seaweed at low tide. This little crab is surprisingly strong when it pinches, so care is needed when handling it.

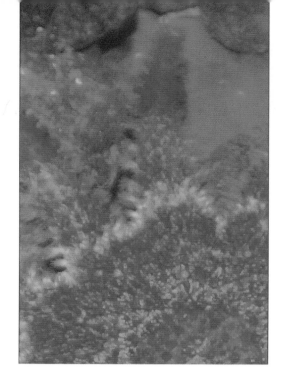

Echinodermata

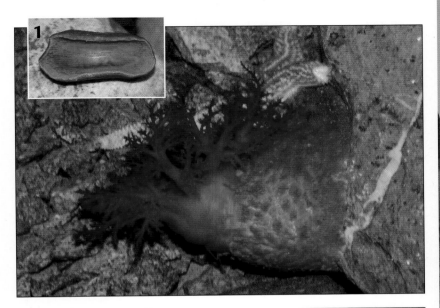

Scarlet psolus
Psolus fabricii

The scarlet psolus, a kind of sea cucumber but with a very hard, scaly skin, is a very striking red colour. It has two small openings, one at each end. One contains 10 tentacles that deploy like feathers to capture plankton. The other is the anus. This cucumber has a flat foot underneath (1), which is used to attach to hard surfaces. It can reach 20 cm.

DISTRIBUTION:
The Arctic to Cape Cod, and in the lower estuary and Gulf of St. Lawrence.

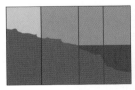

HABITAT:
The subtidal zone, but occasionally in tidal pools.

The scarlet psolus lives mostly on rocky bottoms and likes to hide in sand, with only its tentacles sticking out. Sometimes, it can be seen in tidal pools in the lower intertidal zone.

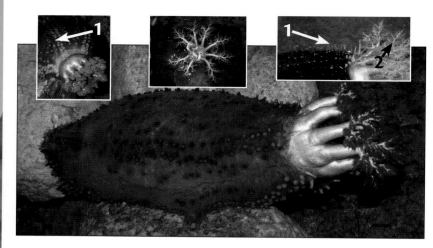

Orange-footed sea cucumber
Cucumaria frondosa

This is an echinoderm shaped like a cucumber, with soft, smooth, but firm skin. It has 5 rows of podia (1) along its body. At one end is the anus. At the other end is the oral opening, which has 10 tentacles (2) resembling feathers. Young individuals are sometimes pale orange. Adults are mostly brown, reddish-brown, or dark purple, often with the tip of the podia a vibrant orange. It can be up to 40 cm long, especially in deeper waters.

DISTRIBUTION:
The Arctic to Cape Cod, including the lower estuary and the Gulf of St. Lawrence.

HABITAT:
Mostly in the subtidal zone, but can be found in tidal pools.

The sea cucumber filters water through its tentacles and feeds on plankton. If it is disturbed, the tentacles completely disappear inside the opening.

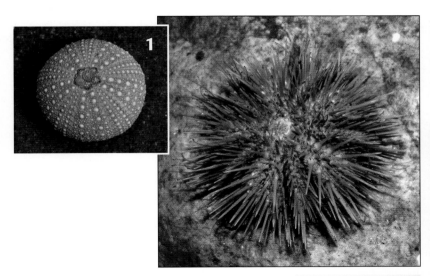

Green sea urchin

Strongylocentrotus droebachiensis

This globular echinoderm has a flattened bottom. The calcareous shell (test) is covered with spines. Five rows of podia are aligned from one pole to the other, around the test. It is pale to dark green, sometimes with reddish-purple hues. The diameter of the test can be up to 9 cm.

DISTRIBUTION:
The upper estuary to the Gulf of St. Lawrence, the Saguenay Fjord, and from the Arctic to New Jersey.

HABITAT:
Very common in tidal pools and in the subtidal zone.

Some urchins can live as long as 25 years. They mainly graze on seaweed, but can feed on animal matter. From great heights, gulls drop urchins on rocks to break them open. After eating them, the gulls leave the empty tests behind, which dry in the sun and lose their spines. The pale green tests (1) then reveal the rows of bumps where the spines used to be.

Sand dollar
Echinarachnius parma

An echinoderm with a round, flat, disk shape, the sand dollar has a uniform carpet of short spines (1) on its surface. When found beached on the sand, it is whitish and has lost its spines (2). At this point, it reveals a 5-petal "flower pattern" on the slightly convex surface, and a small hole in the middle of the other side. When alive, it is reddish-brown or dark brownish-purple. Its diameter can reach 8 cm.

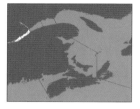

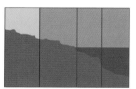

DISTRIBUTION:
Labrador to New Jersey, including the lower estuary and the Gulf of St. Lawrence.

HABITAT:
The subtidal zone, and sometimes in lower intertidal zone inside bays.

The sand dollar, related to the green sea urchin, lives mainly half buried in the sand, on the lookout for food such as small organisms and plankton.

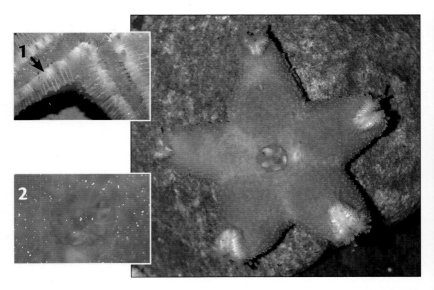

Winged seastar
Pteraster militaris

This brightly coloured seastar has 5 small but very thick arms, covered with a membrane supported by spines (1). On the top of the seastar, there is a hole in the centre (2). The skin feels rough and the body is inflexible. The top of the seastar is a bright red, yellow, or orange, with the underside paler. Sometimes, the tips of the arms are darker. It rarely exceeds 7 cm.

DISTRIBUTION:
The Arctic to Cape Cod, and in the lower estuary and Gulf of St. Lawrence.

HABITAT:
The subtidal zone, but sometimes in the lower intertidal zone.

The space underneath the top membrane of the winged seastar serves as a brooding pouch for young ones. The eggs are deposited there, and when the hatchlings are ready to come out, they poke through the membrane. This is a species that lives mostly in deeper waters, but occasionally, it is found beached on the sand after storms.

Purple sunstar
Solaster endeca

This impressive seastar generally has 9 to 14 arms. The slightly rough skin feels like soft leather. There is an oral opening (1) and rows of small podia (2) underneath the animal. Mostly purple, it can sometimes be pale orange. It can reach a diameter of 25 cm.

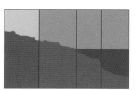

DISTRIBUTION:
The Arctic to Cape Cod, and from the lower estuary to the Gulf of St. Lawrence.

HABITAT:
The subtidal zone, but sometimes in the lower intertidal zone.

Purple sunstars live mostly on rocky and pebbly substrates. They often prey on common seastars.

Spiny sunstar
Crossaster papposus

A spiny seastar has 10 to 14 arms. The surface of the skin is covered with soft, short spines. There are small podia underneath the animal. It is bright red with white or pink concentric bands. The diameter can reach 17 cm.

DISTRIBUTION:
The Arctic to the Gulf of Maine, and from the lower estuary to the Gulf of St. Lawrence.

HABITAT:
In the subtidal zone, but often in the lower intertidal zone

The diet of this star consists of sea urchins, anemones, mollusks, sea cucumbers, and other seastar species. It lives mainly in the rocky subtidal zone, but can be seen in the lower intertidal zone.

Bloodstar
Henricia sp.

This smooth seastar has 5 arms, more slender than those of the common seastar. There are very small podia underneath the animal. Usually reddish-purple, it can be yellow or orange, but also near-white (1). The diameter can reach up to 10 cm.

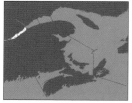

DISTRIBUTION:
The lower estuary to the Gulf of St. Lawrence and Saguenay Fjord, to Cape Hatteras.

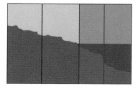

HABITAT:
In the subtidal zone in the southern regions, but common in tidal pools in northern regions.

The bloodstar can absorb nutritional elements directly through the skin, on top of using its stomach on prey. Young females brood their embryos before releasing them into the ocean.

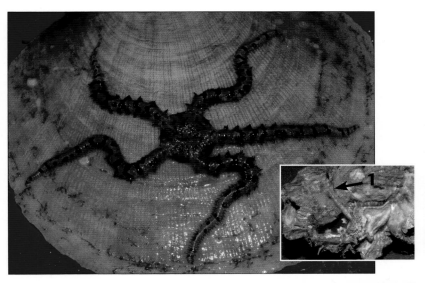

Daisy brittle star
Ophiopholis aculeata

The daisy brittle star is very fragile, with 5 long, slender arms around a central disk. There are several short spines along the edges of each arm, which are flexible and undulate much like a snake. They range from beige to reddish-brown, with a variety of patterns on the arms and disk. The disk can reach up to 1.9 cm in diameter, and the arms more than 8.5 cm long.

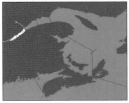

DISTRIBUTION:
The Arctic to Cape Cod, and in the lower estuary and Gulf of St. Lawrence.

HABITAT:
In the lower intertidal zone, often in tidal pools, and in the subtidal zone.

This brittle star hides in the sand and between rocks, and it can also be found curled up inside empty barnacle shells (1). It uses its long arms to capture small crustaceans and organic debris.

Common seastar, Boreal seastar
Asterias vulgaris, Asterias rubens

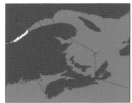

A seastar with five arms, the common seastar has a small white or pale yellow plate (madreporite) (1) near the centre at the top. The skin is rough, with pale, short spines, some of them forming a line down each arm (2). There are several rows of podia underneath the animal

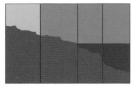

(3). The colour varies greatly: purple, yellow, orange, brown, olive green, red, or almost white. The diameter can reach 40 cm.

Sometimes we also find the Forbes' seastar (*Asterias forbesi*) (4), which lacks the spiny line down the top of the arms, and has an orange madreporite. Another similar species, the Polar seastar (*Leptasterias polaris*) is found in northern regions, and has 6 arms instead of 5.

DISTRIBUTION:
Labrador to Cape Hatteras. In the lower estuary, the Gulf of
St. Lawrence, and the Saguenay Fjord.

HABITAT:
In the intertidal and subtidal zone.

In order to eat, common seastars eject their stomach into their
prey to digest outside of their body. When they eat blue mussels,
they use their powerful arms to pry open the mussel to insert their
stomach (5). On occasion, seastars can lose one or more arms, but
they can regenerate them over a long period of time (6). They live in
the intertidal zone, but move into deeper waters in winter.

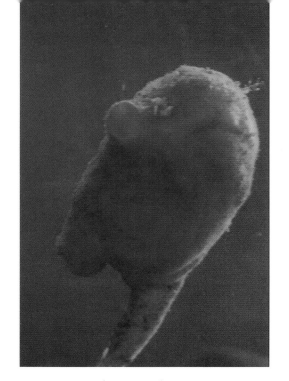

Chordata

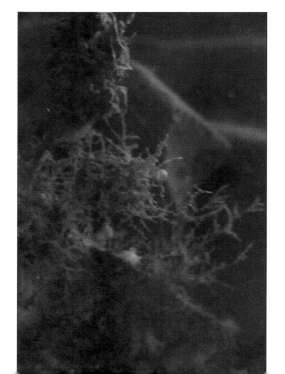

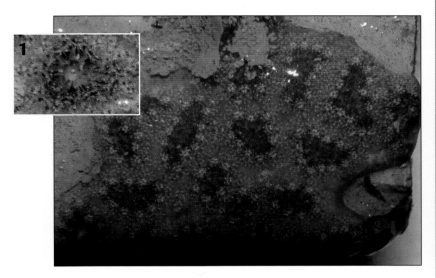

Golden star tunicate, Star sea squirt
Botryllus schlosseri

This tunicate lives in colonies of small individuals, forming an elegant star pattern (1) surrounded by a gelatinous substance. It develops on the surface of rocks, submerged pilings, and seaweed. Each star can contain from 5 to 20 tunicates. The colour varies: purple, brown, beige, sometimes with a golden sheen. The colonies can cover a surface of 7.5 to 10 cm in width.

DISTRIBUTION:
The Bay of Fundy to Chesapeake Bay.

HABITAT:
The lower intertidal zone to the shallow subtidal zone.

Each golden star tunicate has its own siphon to take in seawater to filter food, but it shares the outgoing siphon in the centre of the star with other members of the colony. They are found in bays and tidal pools, and in estuaries where salinity levels may be lower. This species is also found in Europe.

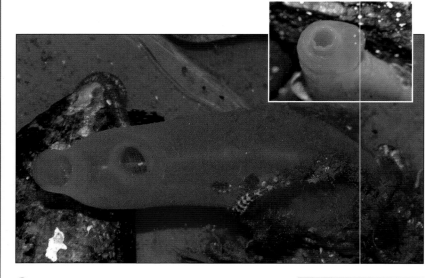

Sea vase
Ciona intestinalis

The sea vase is a beautiful tunicate that is almost transparent, and has the shape of a vase. Sometimes muscle bands are visible on its sides. There are two siphons: one with eight sides, the other with six. At the intersections of these sides is a white or bright yellow edge. The surface of the body is smooth and soft. Translucent, it can sometimes be tinged with yellow. It can occasionally measure 7 cm or more in length.

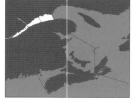

DISTRIBUTION:
The Arctic to Cape Cod, including the Gulf of St. Lawrence.

HABITAT:
Shallow subtidal zone.

The sea vase can retract when disturbed. Out of the water, it is no more than a gelatinous blob. Under water, it attaches to any hard surface, including wharf pilings, boat hulls, rocks, etc.

Sea potato, Stalked sea squirt
Boltenia ovifera

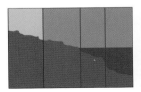

This tunicate resembles the sea peach, but it has a stem (1) with a base that attaches to a hard surface. The stem is 2 to 4 times the length of the body itself. It is usually dark orange, pink or yellow. The body of the sea potato can reach 8 cm.

DISTRIBUTION:
The Arctic to Cape Cod, and from the lower estuary to the Gulf of St. Lawrence.

HABITAT:
Usually in the subtidal zone, but sometimes in the lower intertidal zone.

The sea potato filters seawater to capture plankton. The siphon that points upwards (2) lets water in, and the siphon that points downwards lets water out. This species is very common at the bottom of the ocean, offshore.

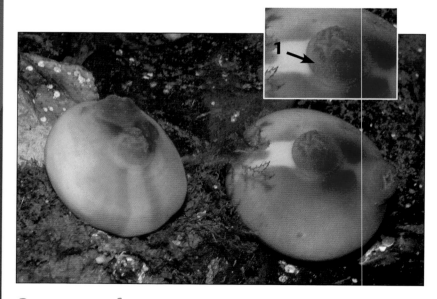

Sea peach
Halocynthia pyriformis

A globular tunicate, the sea peach has 2 prominent siphons (1) at the top. Each siphon has four sides. The surface of the skin feels granular. It can be peach, orange, or pale yellow in colour. It can reach 6 cm, rarely more.

DISTRIBUTION:
The Arctic to Cape Cod, and the lower estuary to the Gulf of St. Lawrence.

HABITAT:
In the subtidal zone, sometimes shallow.

When the sea peach is taken out of the water, it keeps some water inside and feels like a small, hard balloon. It can eject the water through one of its siphons. It attaches to hard surfaces, like rocks and wharf pilings.

Sea grapes
Molgula sp.

A very small globular tunicate, the sea grape's outer skin can sometimes be so encrusted with debris that it masks the whole animal. Without debris, it is translucent, with two tall siphons, one 4-lobed and one 6-lobed, which are widely separated (more so than on the sea vase). The internal organs can often be seen through the skin. Most species of sea grape attach themselves to rocks, boat hulls, seaweed, and other substrates.

They can reach 35 mm in diameter.

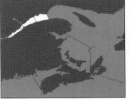

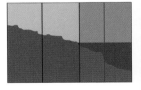

DISTRIBUTION:
Different species can be found from the Arctic to the Gulf of Mexico.

HABITAT:
The lower intertidal and shallow subtidal zones.

Molgula manhattensis, which can be found in the Bay of Fundy, can tolerate brackish and often very polluted waters. As with other delicate tunicates, sea grapes do not hold their shape out of the water.

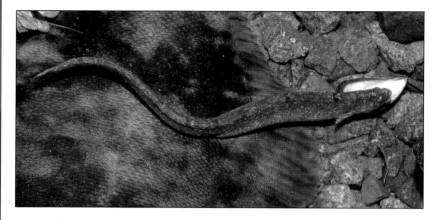

Rock gunnel
Pholis gunnellus

The rock gunnel is a small fish shaped like a flattened ribbon. There are 9 to 13 round spots at the base of the dorsal fin. It can be pale olive green, or brown to reddish-brown, sometimes with stripes. This fish can grow to 25 cm long.

DISTRIBUTION:
Labrador to Delaware Bay. In the lower estuary and the Gulf of St. Lawrence (Bay of Chaleur, NB).

HABITAT:
The lower intertidal zone, including tidal pools, and in the shallow subtidal zone.

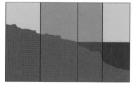

The rock gunnel is one of very few fish that can survive out of water at low tide. It hides under rocks and clumps of seaweed, and breathes air until the water rises again. Its behaviour very much resembles that of the eel.

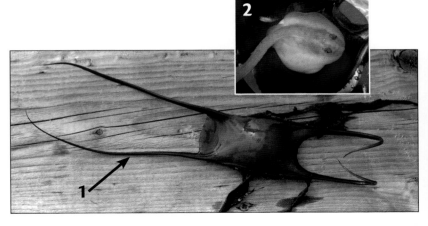

Mermaid's purse

This small, rectangular, smooth envelope with a long hook at each corner (1), shelters the embryo of a skate. The outer skin of the envelope is rather thick, which gives it a soft plastic feel. It is mostly olive green or yellowish-brown. Its size varies according to the species of skate. The smaller ones are 36 to 46 mm in length, but larger ones can reach 100 to 120 mm.

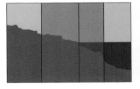

DISTRIBUTION:
The North Atlantic skate species are normally found from the southern part of the Gulf of St. Lawrence to North Carolina. A few species make their way into the estuary of the St. Lawrence River.

HABITAT:
Found empty on the beach, or floating at the surface of the water.

Several species of skate live in the waters off the East Coast. They are oviparous fish, which means they lay eggs. In this case, the egg is in a capsule, or envelope. The embryo, which develops safely inside (2), feeds on its yolk. The hooks help anchor the capsule to substrate at the bottom of the ocean. Some shark species also reproduce the same way using mermaid's purses. Those found on the beach are often empty; the young skates having already left them.

Skates
Rajidae family

Related to sharks, skates are fish with a cartilaginous skeleton instead of bone. The body shape resembles a flat lozenge, with a long narrow tail with small dorsal fins near the tip. Underneath the animal is a mouth and gill slits (1). The eyes are located on the top of the fish. Two fins resembling legs are situated on each side of the tail. Non-venomous spines can be felt along the skate's back, the centre, and around the edges. There are more than 15 species in our region.

DISTRIBUTION:
The Gulf of St. Lawrence (and sometimes the estuary) to North Carolina.

HABITAT:
The shallow subtidal zone.

Skates live at the bottom of the ocean, but we sometimes catch a glimpse of them near the shore in shallow waters. Young skates often come and explore beaches with the waves and occasionally get stuck in tidal pools at low tide. Skates are not shy, but they should be touched with care, as their dorsal spines can be very sharp.

Glossary

Anterior canal: Notch shaped like an elongated funnel at the base of the aperture on a gastropod's shell. The mollusk's siphon is able to come out through this canal.

Apex: The equivalent of the bivalve's umbo. The very top of a gastropod shell.

Axial ribs: Raised ribs that are parallel to a shell's axis on the surface of a gastropod's spire.

Bivalve: Mollusk with a shell consisting of two "valves" closing together to cover the whole animal.

Carapace: The top part of a crustacean's shell, covering the head and thorax.

Chondrophore: spoon-shaped plate located just under the shell's hinge in bivalves, like in the soft-shelled clam.

Columella: Thick axis of a gastropod shell, which starts at the base of the aperture.

Gastropod: Mollusk with a spiral shell, or shell-less, that moves around using a large foot.

Hydrozoans: Group of animals consisting of small cnidarians living mostly in colonies, like the hydroids.

Inner lip: The edge of the aperture that is closest to the body of a gastropod's shell.

Intertidal zone: Maritime zone along the coast covered with seawater at high tide and exposed at low tide.

Lateral teeth: Small prominent ledges on each side of the shell's hinge inside a bivalve.

Lunule: Heart-shaped cavity on the side of certain bivalves, seen just below the umbo when the two valves are closed.

Madreporite: a light-coloured, button-like 'opening' used to filter water into the water-vascular system of echinoderms.

Ombilicus: Small cavity or hole at the base of the columella, immediately beside the aperture of some of the gastropod's shell.

Outer lip: The far edge of the aperture on a gastropod's shell.

Pallial line: Scar left by the muscle of the mollusk on the inside of the shell's surface, parallel to the outer edge (bivalves).

Pallial sinus: V- or U-shaped notch, more or less pronounced, of the pallial line on one or both sides inside of a bivalve's shell.

Plankton: Group of micro-organisms, both plant (phytoplankton) and animal (zooplankton), suspended in the ocean, that drift with the currents.

Podia: Small, elongated, flexible feet with a suction cup at the tip for moving around and manipulating food bits in echinoderms, like seastars.

Rostrum: More or less pointy projection at the front of a carapace, located between the eyes of certain crustaceans.

Spiral cords: Prominent cords that follow the shell's turns, or whorls on the surface of a gastropod's spire.

Spiral ribs: Raised ribs that follow the shell's turns, or whorls on the surface of a gastropod's spire.

Spire: The part of a gastropod's shell that includes all the spiralled whorls.

Subtidal zone: Underwater zone below the low-tide level along the coast, where seaweed still benefit from the sunlight.

Test: Calcareous envelope supporting the external spines of sea urchins and sand dollars, which also protects the internal organs.

Tidal pools: Rocky basins in the intertidal zone that retain seawater at low tide.

Umbo: Beak-shaped bump on top of the hinge of a bivalve's shell.

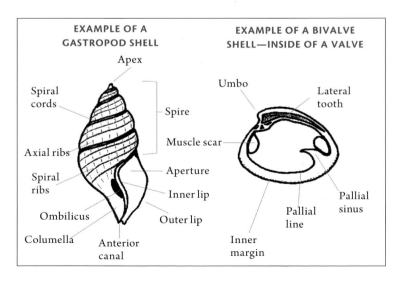

EXAMPLE OF A GASTROPOD SHELL

EXAMPLE OF A BIVALVE SHELL—INSIDE OF A VALVE